Muck

Scoop

Scruffty

Spud

JJ

Dizzy

Farmer Pickles

Skip

Molly

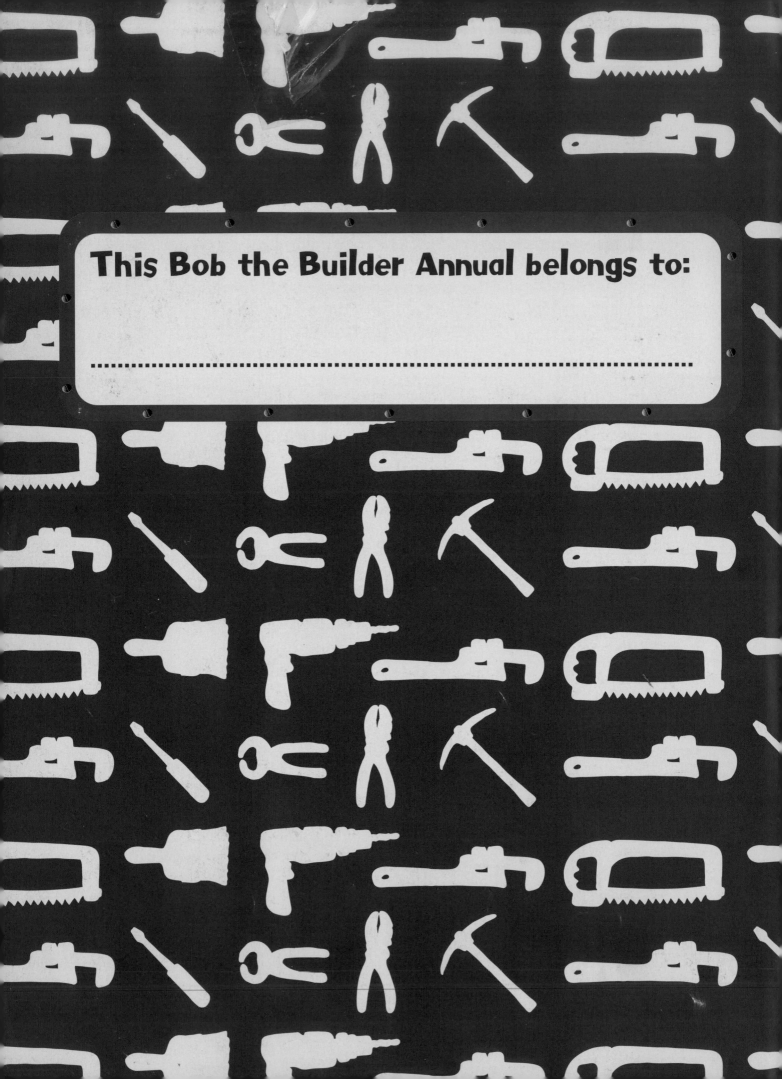

This Bob the Builder Annual belongs to:

....

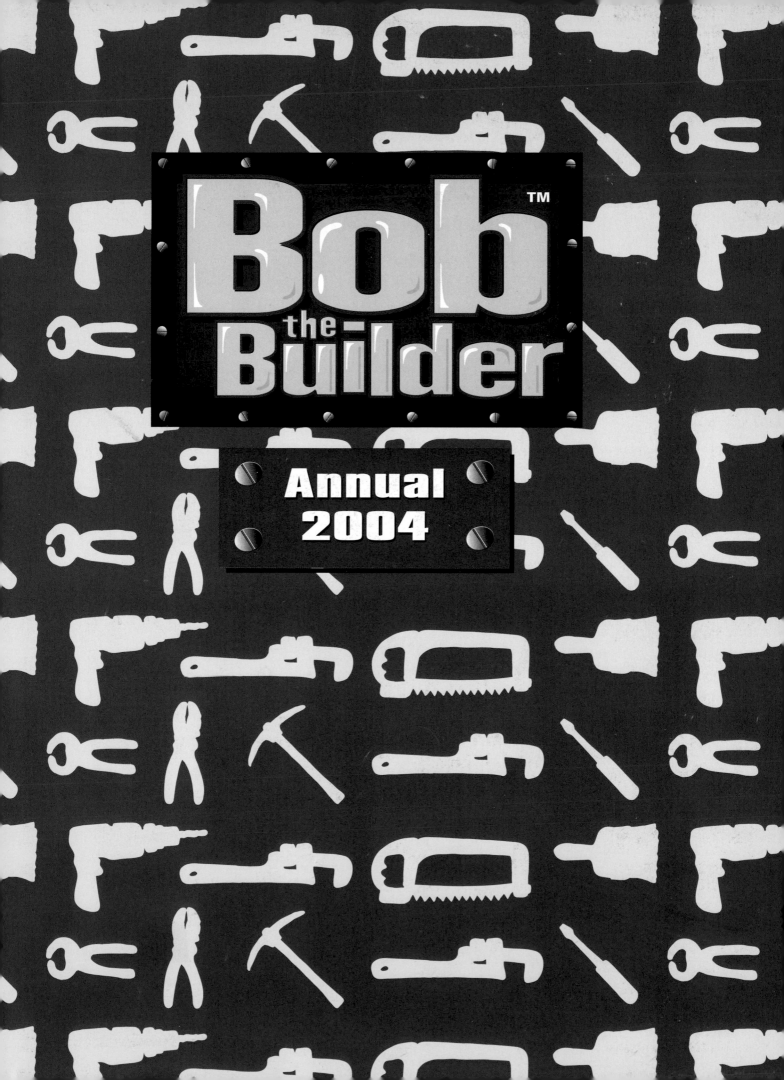

Contents

Don't forget to enter the Bob the Builder Annual competition. There are lots of super prizes for the lucky winners!
You'll find it at the back of the book.

Written by Brenda Apsley   Designed by Sally Metcalfe

Edited by Brenda Apsley and Jane Clempner
Stories adapted from original scripts by Sarah Ball, Glenn Dakin, James Henry, Jimmy Hibbert, Simon Jowett and Lee Price

Based upon the television series **Bob the Builder** © HIT Entertainment PLC and Keith Chapman 2003
With thanks to HOT Animation   Text and illustrations © HIT Entertainment PLC, 2003

www.bobthebuilder.com

Published in Great Britain in 2003 by Egmont Books Limited, 239 Kensington High Street, London W8 6SA
Printed in Dubai, the U.A.E.   ISBN 0 7498 5848 6

"Hello!"

"My name is Bob the Builder. I have a building yard, and I do all sorts of building, making and fixing jobs. It's hard work, but it's fun too. I can't do the jobs on my own, so I have some very special people to help me.

"This is Wendy, my partner in the building yard. She's a very good builder. Some people say she's as good as me! Wendy makes sure that we know which jobs to go to, and that we take the right tools and equipment with us. She's kind and helpful, and we all like her a lot!"

"Meet the Team"

"We couldn't do so many jobs without a lot of help from the machines. They are a very important part of the building yard team. Here they are!"

Scoop is	yellow
Scoop is	a big digger, who's the leader of the team
Scoop is	good at sorting out problems
Scoop likes	playing tricks
Scoop says	"No prob, Bob!"

Muck is	red
Muck is	a digger-dumper
Muck likes	getting as mucky and as messy as he can!
Muck doesn't like	the dark
Muck says	"Muck to the rescue!"

Lofty is   blue
Lofty is   a mobile crane
Lofty is   quiet, and a bit shy
Lofty doesn't like   being high
               up, Spud
               – and mice!
Lofty says   "Ooo-er!"

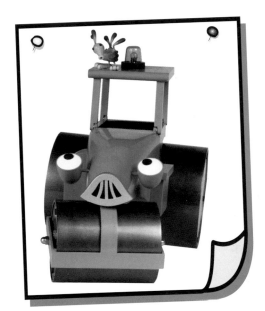

Roley is   green
Roley is   a steam roller
Roley likes   music and singing
Roley loves   his friend, Bird
Roley says   "Rock and roll!"

Dizzy is   orange
Dizzy is   a cement mixer
Dizzy likes   playing football
Dizzy loves   dancing to
               pop music
Dizzy says   "Brilliant!"

Farmer Pickles has a farm just outside the town. We all enjoy going out there to help him.

Farmer Pickles

Spud

This is Spud. He's Farmer Pickles' scarecrow. His job is to scare the birds away from the fields, but he prefers telling jokes and being cheeky! He's got a parsnip for a nose!

Travis is Farmer Pickles' tractor. He's very strong, and he sometimes helps us when there are heavy things to move and pull around.

Travis

I buy all the things I need from **JJ**'s building supplies yard. He likes to keep the yard very neat and tidy, and he knows where every spanner and nail and hammer is!

JJ

Molly

JJ's daughter is called **Molly**. She's at art college, but she works at the yard in her spare time, hiring out the skips.

Trix is JJ's purple forklift truck. She moves so fast that she sometimes forgets what she's doing! She's cheeky, and she loves playing jokes and tricks on people.

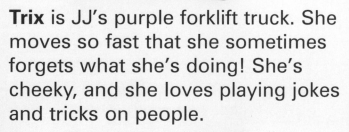

Trix

Skip

When JJ's customers want to hire a skip, **Skip** takes it out to them. When it's full, he takes the skip to the dump, and empties it. He's very useful because he can carry other things, too, using his strong chains.

"Say Hello to My Animal Friends"

Bird is   a bird!
Bird is   blue and red, with a yellow beak

Bird lives   in Bob's yard
Bird likes   his best friend, Roley
Bird loves   singing songs with Roley

Bird says   "Tweet!"

Scruffty is   a dog
Scruffty is   yellow, with black ears, tail – and a big spot!
Scruffty lives on Farmer Pickles' farm
Scruffty likes being cheeky, and getting up to things he shouldn't!
Scruffty loves eating bones, and chasing things – especially rabbits!
Scruffty says "Ruff!"

Pilchard is	a cat
Pilchard is	blue, with black stripes
Pilchard lives	in Bob's house
Pilchard likes	eating fish, and sleeping
Pilchard loves	chasing things – especially mice!
Pilchard says	"Miaow!"

Squawk is	a crow
Squawk is	black
Squawk lives	on Farmer Pickles' farm
Squawk likes	eating seeds and grain
Squawk doesn't like	Spud the scarecrow!
Squawk says	"Squawk!"

Fin is	a goldfish
Fin is	orange
Fin lives	in a goldfish bowl in Bob's house
Fin likes	swimming
Fin says	"Glub!"

Spud the Pilot

One morning, Bob was sorting out the jobs for the day.

"I'm going to replace some tiles on Mrs Broadbent's roof with Scoop and Lofty," said Wendy.

"And I'm going to JJ's with Muck to pick up a new fireplace for Mrs Percival," said Bob. "Come on, everyone."

"**Can we fix it?**" said Scoop.

"**Yes, we can!**" said the others – all except Lofty.

"Er, yeah ... I think so," he said.

Just as Bob and Muck turned into JJ's yard, a little plane buzzed over their heads.

"What do you think of my plane?" said JJ. "She's remote controlled. I can make her do all sorts of things. Watch this!"

JJ worked the controls, and the little plane flew in a circle over their heads.

"Brilliant!" said Muck.

When Bob and Muck had gone off to Mrs Percival's house, JJ took his model plane into the fields. "Now then," he said, pressing a button on the control box. "Let's see what you can do!"

The little plane buzzed, then it raced across the ground, and took off into the air.

It zoomed across the sky ... then turned upside down.

It climbed into the air again ... then dived.

The plane soared into the air ... then looped the loop.

It went faster and faster and faster ... then it disappeared over the treetops!

"Hey!" said JJ, putting down his control box and running after it. "Come back!"

JJ's plane flew into Spud's field and he had to duck out of its way. "Ooooohhh!" he said.

When the plane landed, Spud picked it up and ran around, making plane noises. "**Neown!**" he said. "I'm flying! I'm Spud the pilot. **NEEEOOWWNN!**"

Spud ran faster and faster, then he raced out of the field.

When JJ got there, Spud – and the plane – were nowhere to be seen.

Spud was having fun. **"NEEOOWWNN!"** he said. **"BRRRRRMMMMM!"**

When he found JJ's control box he pressed one of the buttons.

Brrrrm! went the plane.

"A-ha!" said Spud. "Now what if I press this little lever?"

The plane bumped across the grass, then zoomed up into the air!

"HA!" said Spud. "Spud the pilot, flying at twenty squillion feet!"

Spud moved a lever, and the plane turned this way and that, then dropped. Spud smiled. "Hey, I've got a great idea," he said.

Squawk the crow was pecking at the ground when the little plane swooped towards him.

BUZZ went the plane.

"SQUAWK!" said Squawk, jumping out of the way.

The plane turned, and dived at Squawk.

"SQUAWK!" said Squawk.

Spud was watching. "He-he!" he said. "It's easy scaring crows when you're a pilot!"

When the plane zoomed towards him again, Squawk flew off. Spud was right behind him, but he didn't see the log on the ground in front of him, and he tripped over it.

"**OOOF!**" said Spud, dropping the control box, which hit the ground with a **BANG!** and a shower of sparks.

Squawk watched from a tree as the plane flew in little circles. "**ARK! ARK! ARK!**" he laughed.

Spud picked up the control box. "I'll get you this time!" he said, fiddling with the controls.

But the plane didn't head for Squawk – it zoomed off in the opposite direction.

Spud ran after it. "OI!" he shouted. "Come back!"

JJ was still looking for his plane when Spud ran past him.

"Stop that plane!" said Spud.

The plane flew into town, and Spud was right behind it. It flew towards Mrs Percival's house, and buzzed round the chimney ...

Inside, Bob and Mrs Percival were looking at her new fireplace. "Thanks, Bob," she said. "It's lovely. And there's no mess at all, so I can put these dust sheets away."

But just then, a cloud of thick black soot burst out of the fireplace, followed by what was left of JJ's model plane.

"OH!" said Mrs Percvial. "What happened? I can't see a thing!"

Bob coughed. "What the ..."

Slowly, the black soot began to settle. It covered the carpet, the furniture – and Bob and Mrs Percival!

Bob picked up the plane. "This looks like JJ's," he said.

"Then I want a word with him," said Mrs Percival.

Spud was outside.

Bob held out the plane. "Do you know anything about this?" asked Mrs Percival.

"Me?" said Spud. "Er ... no, well, not exactly! See, I found the plane, an' I scared Squawk with it, but I tripped on a log ... an' it flew away, an' it all went wrong!"

Just then, JJ arrived. "You found my plane, Spud!" he said. "But where are the wings?"

Spud pointed to where the wings were sticking out of the chimney. "They're up there," he said. "Sorry."

"Never mind," said Bob. "I'll use the long ladder to get the wings down, and I'll repair your plane, JJ."

"But what about all the mess?" said Mrs Percival.

Bob looked hard at Spud. "I think you need some help," he said.

"Yeah, you need help," said Spud. Then he realised who Bob had in mind. "Oh, you mean me, Bob? Yeah, OK, Spud's on the job!"

Spud was soon busy cleaning Mrs Percival's house. But he was having fun, too, using his feather duster as a plane!

"**Neeeoooowwwn!**" said Spud. "I bet real pilots don't have to do the dusting! **NEEOOOWWNN!**"

Molly's Picture Puzzle

Wendy

Lofty's eye

JJ

window

tree

Bob

gas mask

Lofty's grabber

"Here's a fun puzzle for you! Look at the little pictures on this page. How many of them can you see in the big picture on the next page? Point, and say the words out loud."

Mr Beasley's New Friends

Do you like telling stories? First, listen to this story about Mr Beasley. Now, can you point to each picture, starting at number 1, and tell the story again, in your own words this time?

"Mr Beasley, will you look after my pigeons for me?" says Mr Dixon.

1

2

"Yes," says Mr Beasley. But the pigeons make a mess. Naughty pigeons!

3 "I'll build a special house for the pigeons," says Wendy.

4 But the little house is empty. The pigeons don't like it!

5 "Coo!" they say. "We want to stay with Mr Dixon!"

6 "Never mind," says Mr Beasley. "The house is perfect for my new **BAT** friends!"

Note to parents: Storytelling is a key pre-reading and early-learning skill. Read the story with your child, pointing to the pictures as you read each piece of text out loud, using lots of expression in your voice. Now, encourage your child to tell **you** the story, by pointing to each picture in turn and retelling the story in his or her own words. Make 'reading' fun!

Bob and the Badgers

1   When Bob gave Pilchard her breakfast one morning, she soon ate it all up. "Anyone would think you'd never been fed before!" said Bob. "**MIAOW!**" said Pilchard.

2   Pilchard scratched at the back door. She wanted to go out. "I'll fit that cat flap I promised you," said Bob. "**MIAOW-OW!**" said Pilchard. What a good idea!

3   Some other animals were having breakfast, too – rabbits were busy eating Farmer Pickles' lettuces! "OI!" he said. "Shoo!" "**WOOF! GRR!**" said Scruffty.

4   Pilchard wanted to see her new cat flap. "Sorry, it will have to wait," said Bob. "We have to make a fence to stop the rabbits eating Farmer Pickles' lettuces."

5 Bob and the team worked hard. They dug a trench and put a tall wire fence in it, then Scoop pushed the soil back into the trench. "Good job!" said Wendy.

6 "I hope it keeps the rabbits out," said Bob. "Spud's going to keep watch tonight – just in case," said Farmer Pickles. "Yeah," said Spud, "Spud's on the job!"

7 Spud waggled his hands like rabbit ears. Then he hopped into the field. "Hippety hop, hippety hop," he said. "Just look at my rabbit disguise!"

8 That night the rabbits got a surprise when they saw the fence. They climbed on top of each other, but they couldn't get over the fence. "Shoo!" said Spud.

9 The rabbits gave up and hopped away. "Rabbit scaring is hard work," said Spud. "**YAWN!** I'll just have a little lie down." He was soon fast asleep: **ZZZZZ.**

10 Spud had visitors that night – but not the rabbits. While he slept, two badgers pushed against the fence, and knocked it down! Spud didn't hear a thing!

11 Farmer Pickles wanted to know how the rabbits had got in again. "**WOOF!**" Scruffty showed him the broken fence. "OO-ER. Something BIG did that," said Spud.

12 Farmer Pickles told Wendy about the fence. "I'll fix it, Bob," said Wendy. "You can fit Pilchard's cat flap." "**MIAOW!**" said Pilchard. About time too!

13 Spud showed Farmer Pickles some big footprints he had found. "They're very big," said Spud. "Real monster footprints. I ... I was lucky it didn't EAT me!"

14 "They're not made by sheep," said Farmer Pickles. "I'll look for clues. You keep an eye on the rabbits." Spud gulped. "But what if the m-monster comes?"

15 "Don't be silly," said Farmer Pickles. "There are no such things as monsters." Wendy smiled. "But Scoop can stay here with you, just in case." "Okay then," said Spud.

16 **SNIFF!** Scruffty followed a scent to a tree. "**WOOF!**" "Look, Wendy, something's been scratching at the tree," said Farmer Pickles. "Good work, Scruffty!"

17 "Here's another clue," said Dizzy. "Black and white hairs caught on the tree guard." Now Farmer Pickles knew who the visitors were – badgers!

18 Scruffty followed another trail to a big hole. "Badgers always use the same paths," said Farmer Pickles. "They went through my lettuces to the stream."

19 "But the fence was in the way, so they pushed it down!" said Wendy. "How can we stop the rabbits without stopping the badgers getting to the stream?"

20 Wendy rang Bob to see if he could help. Just then, Pilchard jumped through her new cat flap. "I think I know what to do," said Bob. "I'll be right over."

21 Bob cut the wire fence and made it into a flap. "There!" he said, "a cat flap – for badgers! The little rabbits can't open it, but the big badgers can!"

22 "**WOOF!**" said Scruffty. Can I try it? "Yes," said Bob. "You have a go, Scruffty." Scruffty pushed the flap with his head, and walked through. "Brilliant!" said Dizzy.

23 That night, Bob and the others went back to the lettuce field. They wanted to see if the badgers would be clever enough to use the flap Bob had made for them.

24 One of the badgers used his paws to push the flap open, then the others followed him through. "Clever badgers!" whispered Muck. "Clever Bob!" said Wendy.

Bob's Jigsaw Pictures

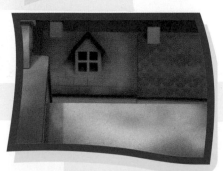

"Can you help me find the little jigsaw pieces that fit into the big pictures on these pages?"

Trix and the Otters

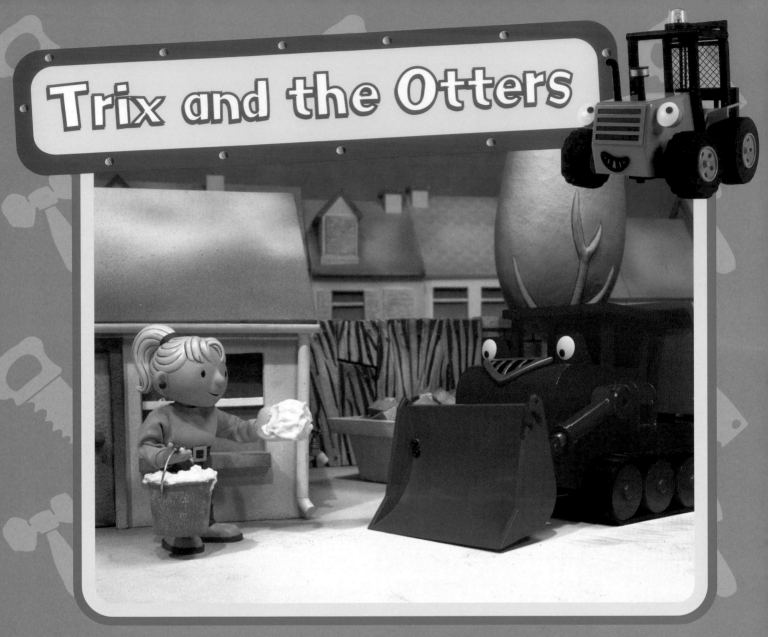

One day, Wendy was washing windows when she splashed some soapy water on Muck.

"Aaargh!" said Muck. "Careful, Wendy, you're splashing soapy water all over me!"

Wendy laughed. "Sorry, Muck. Have I made a clean spot? Shall I clean the rest of you?"

Muck liked being messy, so he didn't like the sound of that. "No thanks, Wendy. I'm fine as I am – honest!"

Just then, Farmer Pickles arrived. Scruffty ran into the yard and put his paws on Muck's shovel. "**Woof! Woof!**"

"Hello, Scruffty," said Muck. "Wow, you're very dirty, aren't you? REALLY messy!"

Scruffty loved being mucky, too. "**Ruff-ruff!**" said Scruffty. Yes I am!

Farmer Pickles had a job for Bob and the team. "I need a new fence around my compost heap," he said. "It's where I put old plants and bits of food. They rot down to make compost, and I put it on my crops to help them grow. But Scruffty likes to roll around in it, so I need a fence to keep him out."

"What a mucky job," said Dizzy. "It sounds yucky."

"OOO, it sounds like a LOVELY job to me!" said Muck.

Scruffty agreed. "**Ruff-ruff!**"

"I'll ring JJ and order the fence," said Wendy.

"Thanks, Wendy," said Bob. "Come on, Muck, Lofty."

"**Can you fix it?**" said Scoop.

"**Yes we can!**" said Muck.

"Er ... yeah ... I think so," said Lofty.

JJ's daughter, Molly, was going to do some painting at the pond, so when Trix took the fence to Farmer Pickles' farm, she gave her a lift.

"I'm going to watch the animals, then draw them," Molly told Trix.

"CAN I WATCH THEM TOO?" shouted Trix.

"Ssshhh!" said Molly. "Quiet, Trix! You've scared the rabbits away! No, not now. You've got that fence to deliver, so off you go."

When Trix got to the farm, Scruffty flicked some compost at her.

"Hey, careful," said Trix. "You may want to look like a compost heap, but I don't!"

"**Woof!**" said Scruffty.

When Scruffty got even more excited, he put his muddy, messy paws all over Trix.

"Oh, no! Not again!" said Trix.

"**Woof!**" said Scruffty.

Bob wiped the muck off Trix. "You go back to JJ's now," he said.

"Good idea, Bob," said Trix. "It's cleaner there!"

Molly was sitting by the pond when she heard a splash.

"Look, Bird, it's an otter!" said Molly. "And she's got two babies with her!"

One of the otter cubs slid down the bank into the water. "The mother otter is teaching the babies to swim!" Molly whispered.

Just then, Trix crashed through the bushes and shouted, "ARE YOU HAVING A GOOD TIME, MOLLY?"

The otters ran away, and Bird flew off and sat in a tree.

Molly sighed. "Oh, Trix," she said.

"WHAT'S WRONG?" said Trix.

"You made so much noise that you scared the otters away," said Molly.

"Otters?" said Trix. "I want to see them."

"Okay," said Molly. "But you'll have to hide in the bushes. And you'll have to be VERY quiet."

Soon the otters came back, but Trix couldn't see them. "I need to get a bit closer ..." she said.

But when the otters heard Trix's wheels and saw her shiny purple paint, they ran off again.

"The otters don't like me," said Trix. "I'm in the way. I'll just ... go away. 'Bye."

Bob had finished the fence when Farmer Pickles arrived.

Muck made the compost into a neat pile, but Scruffty dived into it, spreading it all over the place.

Soon Muck and Scruffty were both covered in compost. They were very messy, and very mucky – which is just how they like it!

"We'll be off now, Farmer Pickles," said Bob.

"Goodbye, lovely compost," said Muck.

Bob, Muck and Lofty met Trix on the road near the pond. She looked very sad.

"What's wrong?" asked Bob.

"I wanted to see the otters, but they don't like me," said Trix. "They ran away."

"Otters?" said Muck. "I want to see them, too! Come on, Trix."

The otters were rolling around in the mud on the bank of the pond. "They love mud, just like me, Molly!" whispered Muck.

Trix was behind him. "It's not fair!" she said. "Why doesn't Muck scare the otters, but I do?"

"I know why!" said Molly. "The otters can't see Muck because he's so mucky. His red paint is covered in compost, so he's the same brown colour as the mud on the bank."

"Yes!" said Trix. "The otters aren't scared of Muck because they can't see him!"

She turned to Muck. "Do you want to visit your compost heap again?"

"Yeah!" said Muck.

"So do I," said Trix. "Come on!"

Farmer Pickles gave Trix some compost.

"Muck, Scruffty, will you help me get messy?" asked Trix. "REALLY messy?"

"Of course we will!" said Muck. "**Wheeee!**"

"**Woof, woof!**" said Scruffty. This is fun!

Trix, Muck and Scruffty skidded around in the compost. They spun and slid and splashed around until all three of them were covered in compost.

SPLAT!
SPLASH!

Muck and Scruffty were as messy as they had ever been.

Trix was messier still! "Come on," she said. "Back to the pond!"

This time, the otters took no notice of Trix.

"The otters DO like me!" said Trix.

"So do I," said Muck.

Problems for JJ and Molly

"These pictures of Trix look the same, but one of them is different. Can you point to the odd one out?"

"Which of these pictures of Skip is the odd one out? Can you show me?"

Pilchard's Pets

"Read this story with me. When you see a picture, say the word."

Mr Bentley has a job for  and

 and the team.

Wendy

"We want you to build a pets' corner for animals," says Mr Bentley.

"Wow!" says  .

Dizzy

"**Can we fix it?**" says  .

Scoop

"**Yes we can!**" say and

Muck

 and  .

Dizzy   Roley

"Er ... yeah, I think so," says  .

Lofty

The animals are on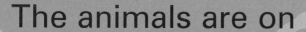

farm. He puts them in the  and

fixes it to  the tractor.

There's a  and a

and a  and a .

"Don't forget Charlie the chinchilla,"

says  .

"I won't," says  .

 and take

the animals to the park.

 **Bob** needs more fencing.

Wendy and  **Muck** go to get

some from **JJ** .

When  **Spud** and  **Travis** get

to the park, the fence is not

ready, so they take the

animals to  **Bob** 's yard.

"Baa!" says the  **sheep** .

"Quack!" says the duck.

"Cluck!" says the **hen** .

"Argh!" says **Lofty** . "Help!"

The animals run around. But clever  knows what to do.

Pilchard

She puts them in a shed.

But Charlie runs away!

Charlie

Later, Travis takes the animals

to the park. But where is Charlie ?

Charlie

Pilchard finds him in the office.

Pilchard

"Well done, Pilchard," says Bob .

Pilchard

Bob

"Miaow!" says Pilchard.

"Eep, eep!" says Charlie .

Charlie

Have Fun with Lofty

"Ooo-er!" said Lofty when the animals from the pets' corner ran round and round Bob's yard. "There are too many of them! And they're making all sorts of funny noises. Help!"

Making animal noises is fun! Can you point to the animals in the picture, and make noises for them? You can do Lofty's voice, too, if you like!

baaa!

cluck!

quack!

miaow!

Bob and the Goalie

One day, Bob was moving a box of paint tins across the yard when Mr Dixon arrived.

"Morning, Bob," said Mr Dixon. "You look like you need a hand. Maybe you're not fit enough."

"Well," said Bob, "my work does keep me **quite** fit ..."

"It's not just you who needs to keep fit," said Mr Dixon. "But here comes Mr Bentley. He'll tell you all about my idea."

"Good morning," said Mr Bentley. "Mr Dixon has had a really good idea. He wants to get the

whole town fit, so we're going to open a new exercise park, with changing rooms. And we want you to build it!" He unrolled a large roll of paper. "Here are the plans!"

"**Wow!**" said Dizzy.

"An exercise park, fantastic!" said Roley.

"That's not all," said Mr Dixon. "My brother, David Dixon, is going to open it for us!"

"David Dixon, the famous goalkeeper?" said Muck.

"**Wow!**" said Lofty.

"I'll order the materials from JJ

right away," said Bob.

"**Can we build it?**" said Scoop.

"**Yes we can!**" said the others.

All except Lofty. "Er, yeah ... er, I think so," he said.

The machines were very excited about David Dixon's visit. They were playing football in the yard when Spud arrived.

Dizzy kicked the ball to him. "Come on, Spud! Take a shot!" she said.

But Spud didn't kick the ball. He picked it up and threw it back to Dizzy. "No, er, I'm just too ... er, good for you," he said, running out of the yard. "See you!"

Building the exercise park kept the team very busy.

Dizzy poured cement for the changing room floor.

Muck brought the ready-made walls.

Lofty helped Bob fix the walls together.

Scoop dug holes for the climbing frame, then Bob fixed it in place.

"It looks just like a football goal!" said Dizzy.

She took the football she had brought in her mixer and threw it to Bob. "Come on, Bob," she said. "I'll be the goalkeeper. Shoot!"

"Sorry, Dizzy," said Bob. "Not today."

Dizzy was disappointed. "Spud didn't want to play, either," she said.

"That's not like him," said Bob. "You'll have to play with Lofty instead."

Later on, Bob was sitting under a tree eating his lunch when Spud arrived and sat down next to Bob.

"Dizzy said you didn't want to play football with her," said Bob. "Why's that?"

"It's because I'm terrible at football," said Spud. "I didn't want the machines to know. They might laugh at me."

"I know just what you mean," said Bob. "I'm useless at football, too."

"Maybe we should help each other," said Spud. "You know what they say – practice makes perfect. We can have a game without the others seeing us. We'll use one of your oranges as a ball."

Spud headed the orange, but it ended up on the end of his parsnip nose!

Bob took a big kick at the orange, but he missed it, and landed on his bottom!

Spud kicked the orange, and Bob dived on it, but he squashed it flat! "Oops!" said Bob. "Game over, I think!"

Spud laughed, and kicked the orange so hard that it flew off into the park ...

When Muck got back to the yard, he had some news for Wendy. "The exercise park's almost finished!" he told her.

Just then, Mr Dixon arrived with his brother, David.

"It's so kind of you to open the park for us," said Wendy. "I was just going up there to see it. You can come with us."

When they got to the park, Bob and the team were tidying up.

"This is David Dixon," said Wendy.

The machines were very excited.

"They want to play football with you, David," said Wendy.

David stood in the climbing frame 'goal'. "Come on, then, who wants a shot?"

"Me!" said Dizzy. She shot the ball towards the corner of the goal, but David saved it.

"Anyone else fancy a go?" said David. "What about you, Bob?"

"Oh ... er ... I'd rather let ..." said Bob.

"Go on Bob!" said Wendy.

"Back of the net!" said Scoop.

Bob sighed. He went to take a shot, but slipped on the squashed orange he and Spud had used for their game. His other leg hit the ball hard, REALLY hard, and it zoomed towards the goal, hit the post, and bounced out again!

"Bad luck, Bob!" said Dizzy. "It's your turn now, Spud."

"Yeah, go, Spud, go!" said Muck.

"Spud, Spud, Spud, Spud!" said Scoop and Dizzy.

Spud pulled a face, and ran up to the ball. He kicked it as hard as he could – and it flew straight up into the air!

David watched it. So did Bob and the team.

Poor Spud put his hands over his eyes, so he didn't see the ball come down ... bounce off a bucket and send it flying across the grass ... hit the changing room door ... and smack into the crossbar of the goal! Then – **BOING!** – the ball hit a tree, bounced off the parallel bars, hit the fence ... and rolled towards the goal!

David saw it coming, but he couldn't move, because his foot was stuck in the bucket! He hopped towards the ball, fell over

... and the ball rolled into the goal!

"**GOOOAAALL!**" said Spud. "Spud the striker! I told you I was good, didn't I?"

"Well done," said Bob. "We were both a bit lucky today, weren't we?"

Spud laughed. "Speak for yourself, Bob!"

When David got his foot out of the bucket he went over to join them. "Great shooting!" he said. "I can honestly say I've NEVER seen shots quite like yours before!"

51

Dizzy the Sheepdog

Telling stories is good fun! First, listen to this story about Dizzy. Now, point to each picture, starting at number 1, and tell the story again, in your own words this time. Don't forget to make funny noises for Scruffty and the sheep!

1

It's cold and snowy, so Bob builds a new barn for Farmer Pickles' sheep.

2

But one sheep is missing. "**WOOF!**" says Scruffty, and goes to look for it.

3 "Wait for me!" says Dizzy, and she rushes off to help him.

4 They find the sheep – with a new baby lamb! Dizzy takes them back, just like a sheepdog!

5 "Baa! Baa!" The sheep like the new barn. It will keep them warm.

6 "Baa!" They like the soft hay Muck brings, too. It will make a cosy bed!

Note to parents: Storytelling is a key pre-reading and early-learning skill. Read the story with your child, pointing to the pictures as you read each piece of text out loud, using lots of expression in your voice. Now, encourage your child to tell **you** the story, by pointing to each picture in turn and retelling the story in his or her own words. Make 'reading' fun!

Dizzy and Muck Go Camping

1 One morning, Farmer Pickles and Travis went to Bob's yard. "Are you starting work on my new farm camp site today, Bob?" asked Farmer Pickles.

2 "I am, but Wendy's off on holiday with Jenny," said Bob. "We're all packed," said Wendy. "Then we'd better get to the airport," said Bob. "Come on!"

3 The machines were glad about the holiday, but Dizzy looked sad. "Wendy and Jenny are lucky to be going on holiday," she said. "I wish I was going with them."

4 Roley sang a song to cheer Dizzy up, and she joined in. They were still singing when Bob got back from the airport. "Come on," he said. "We've got work to do."

5 Bob and the team went to Farmer Pickles' meadow. "This is where we're going to build the camp site," said Bob. "But what IS a camp site, Bob?" asked Dizzy.

6 "It's where people go for a holiday," said Bob. "They put up tents to sleep in. They cook on a camp fire, and sing songs." Dizzy whizzed around. "Brilliant!"

7 "We'll build the shower block first," said Bob. "But before that, I've got to get all these sheep into that pen." There were sheep everywhere! "**Baaa! Baaaa!**"

8 Farmer Pickles came to see how Bob was getting on. "It's taking longer without Wendy," said Bob. "Then why not come back tomorrow?" said Farmer Pickles.

9 "I will," said Bob. But Dizzy didn't want to go home. "Can I camp here tonight with Muck?" she asked. "I don't see why not!" said Farmer Pickles.

10 Bob made a frame and put one of Farmer Pickles' hay stack covers over it. "That will keep you warm and dry," he said. "Our very own tent!" said Dizzy.

11 That night, Dizzy and Muck heard a noise. "Listen," said Muck, "someone's coming!" It was Spud. "Come and sit by our pretend camp fire," said Dizzy.

12 "I love pretending!" said Spud. "I'll pretend I'm cooking sausages – all for me." "And we can sing a camp fire song," said Dizzy. "Come on, all together now!"

13 "That was fun!" said Spud. "But it's late, and I'm tired, so I'd better go back to the barn." Dizzy opened the gate of the sheep pen for him. "'Night, Spud."

14 Loud noises woke Dizzy and Muck in the morning. "**BAAA!**" There were sheep everywhere! "Oh, no!" said Dizzy. "I forgot to close the gate last night!"

15 Dizzy and Muck tried to round up the sheep. "We need to do it like Scruffty," said Dizzy. She made barking noises. "**Ruff! Ruff!**" So did Muck. "**Ruff! Ruff! Ruff!**"

16 The sheep went back into the pen, but just then, the real Scruffty arrived – and Farmer Pickles was with him. "What's going on here?" he asked.

17 "I'm sorry, I left the gate open last night," said Dizzy. "But we got the sheep back in the pen," said Muck. Farmer Pickles smiled and said, "There's no harm done then."

18 When Bob and Lofty arrived, Bob said, "Hello, Dizzy. Hello, Muck! How are my happy campers this morning?" "We had a brilliant time," said Dizzy. "Great!" said Muck.

19 "Glad to hear it," said Bob. "Now, **can we build it?**" "**Yes we can!**" said Muck and Dizzy. "Er, yeah, I, er, think so ..." said Lofty.

20 Bob and the team were soon hard at work on the shower block. Bob made a floor and built the brick walls, and Dizzy mixed lots and lots of cement.

21 When Lofty put the roof on the walls, the shower block was finished. "That was hard work," said Bob. "I think I'll just sit down for a minute and have a rest ..."

22 Bob sat on the sacks in Dizzy and Muck's tent. It was so warm and cosy that he was soon making snoring noises: **ZZZZZZZ!** "He's fast asleep!" said Dizzy.

23 When Farmer Pickles arrived, Bob was still asleep. "Are you camping, too?" he asked. Bob woke up. "I was ... er ... just ... er ... waiting for you," he said.

24 "You've done a great job," said Farmer Pickles. "And we had a great time!" said Dizzy. "I can't wait to tell Wendy about our camping holiday!"

Wendy's Postcard Puzzle

Roley

Muck

Dizzy

Lofty

Scoop

Wendy sent lots of postcards when she went on holiday.

Follow the mixed-up lines with your finger to find out which name goes with which postcard. Now, draw a little picture on each postcard, or write a name.

Snowman Scoop

It was winter time, and Bob's yard was covered in a blanket of soft white snow.

"It's the Best Snowman Contest this afternoon," said Scoop. "I'm going to make my snowman right now."

"Sorry, Scoop, but your snowman will have to wait," said Bob. "A water pipe has burst outside Mr Sabatini's pizza shop, and there's ice all over the road. I need you, Roley and Dizzy to help me mend the pipe, and put some grit on the road."

"We'll ALL help build a snowman when you get back," said Muck.

"Great!" said Scoop. "We'll do the job AND win the contest! **Can we fix it?**"

"**Yes we can!**" said the others.

"Er ... yeah ... er ... **oof!**" said Lofty – as Muck hit him with a snowball. "That was cold!"

Dizzy couldn't wait to get started on the job. She zoomed off, but skidded on the icy road, and spun round and round. "**Whoa!**" she cried. "It's all slippy!"

Bob laughed. "That's why we

put grit on the ice! Now, let's get this pipe replaced."

Bob and the team dug up the road and took out the old pipe. They put in a new one, and Roley rolled on some new cement. Then they put lots of grit on the road.

"Good-a work, Bob!" said Mr Sabatini. "Now I can-a finish my-a snowman."

Mr Sabatini gave his snowman a big chef's hat made of pizza dough, olives for eyes, a moustache made of chilli peppers – and a pointy carrot nose!

"Let's get back to the yard," said Scoop. "We've got a snowman to make, too!"

Spud was having fun in the snow. He threw a snowball at a snowman, and knocked its hat off, then danced around happily. "Snowball Spud hits the target!"

He stopped when he noticed two rabbits and two field mice watching him.

"Hello," said Spud. "Hey, you look cold – and hungry, too, but I

haven't got any food for you."

Spud looked at the snowman. "Or have I?"

When Bob and the team got back to the yard, Wendy was waiting for them. "Mrs Potts is snowed in," she told them. "Can you take this shopping for her?"

"We'll need your snowplough for this job, Scoop," said Bob.

"No prob, Bob," said Scoop.

On the way, they passed Mr Sabatini's shop. He looked upset. "Mamma mia!" he said. "My snowman, 'ee is a-ruined.

Somebody steal-a 'ees carrot nose!"

"I wonder why?" said Scoop.

When Bob and Scoop had cleared the snow for Mrs Potts, she showed them her snowman. "He's got lots of scarves," said Mrs Potts, "a teapot hat, and ... oh, look, his carrot nose has gone!"

"Just like Mr Sabatini's snowman!" said Scoop.

Bob's mobile phone rang. "We have to help Wendy and Muck rescue Travis," said Bob. "He was taking food out to the animals with the trailer, but got stuck in the snow."

"But what about our snowman?" said Scoop.

"Sorry, Scoop," said Bob, "but this should be our last job today."

Travis was stuck in the top field – but not for long. Scoop cleared a path with his snowplough, then Muck pulled him free using his chain.

The team were about to go back to the yard when Scoop said, "Look, Bob, another snowman. And his nose is missing, just like the others. But this time we can find the thief, because he's made footprints in the snow. I'm going to follow them!"

Scoop followed the footprints into the next field, where he found Spud – and a big bucket of carrots!

"SPUD!" Scoop shouted.

Poor Spud! He leapt into the

air, and slid down the hill.

"OOOOOF!" He ended up in a deep bank of snow.

Scoop pulled him out. "Spud, why did you take the carrot noses from the snowmen?" he asked. "You've spoiled the contest."

"What contest?" asked Spud.

"The Best Snowman Contest," said Scoop.

Just then, some rabbits crept up to the carrots, and started nibbling at them.

"I took the carrots for the animals," said Spud. "They're really hungry. But I haven't got enough food for them."

"I think I can help," said Scoop. "Come on!"

Scoop told Bob and Wendy about the carrots. "I'm going to stay and help Spud feed the animals," he said.

"But what about the contest?" asked Bob.

"This is much more important," said Scoop. "Travis, can I have some of the animal feed in your trailer? I'll take it to the animals in my scoop."

"Of course you can," said Travis.

"Scoop isn't going to win the snowman prize," said Wendy.

"He might, if we help," said Bob. "Look, take some carrots from Travis' trailer, and I'll explain my plan ..."

Bob and Wendy got busy.

Wendy gave Mrs Potts and Mr Sabatini new carrot noses for their snowmen. They gave her things in return. But what were they?

Bob and Lofty piled up a big mound of snow in the yard. But what were they making?

Scoop found out when he got back to the yard.

Mr Bentley was there. "I'm here to judge the last entry in the Best Snowman Contest," Mr Bentley told him.

"I didn't have time to build a snowman," said Scoop.

"BUT WE DID!" cried Bob, pulling a blue blanket from a huge snowman. "SURPRISE!"

"WOW!" said Scoop. "It's brilliant!"

"Mrs Potts gave us a top hat and a scarf for him," said Dizzy.

"And Mr Sabatini gave us his pipe, and potatoes for his eyes," said Wendy.

"But he's got no nose!" said Scoop.

"Yes he has," said Wendy. "We saved a carrot for you to give him. Here, put it on."

Mr Bentley looked at the snowman and smiled. Then he gave it a rosette. "I declare this snowman the winner – by a nose!"

Spot the Differences with Spud

These two pictures of Spud's rabbit friends look the same, but there are three things that are different in picture 2. Can you spot the differences?

"I hope you liked reading all about me and my friends! Goodbye, and see you next year!"

Competition Time!

"Take part in my easy
to enter competition.
Answer the simple question
on the opposite page."